FRÉDÉRIC CHOPIN

(1810 - 1849)

SELECTED WORKS FOR PIANO
BOOK ONE
Compiled and Edited by Keith Snell

CONTENTS

For supplementary study, a recording of this collection is available on compact disc, performed by pianist Diane Hidy (GP390CD). Ms. Hidy's interpretations follow this edition closely as a practical example for students.

ISBN 0-8497-6199-9

FRÉDÉRIC CHOPIN (1810 - 1849)

Frederic Chopin was born in Zelazowa Wola, Poland - a small village near Warsaw - on February 22, 1810. His father, Nicholas, was a native of Marainville, France, and moved to Warsaw to teach French at the Lyceum (high school). His mother, Justyna Krzyzanowska, was Polish. Chopin was the youngest of four children- he had three sisters. Chopin's mother and his sister Louise played the piano, and it was from them that Chopin received his introduction to music.

Chopin was a child prodigy at the piano. Some say that his talent rivaled that of Mozart. By the age of 8, he played his first public concert - a piano concerto by Gyrowetz- and had already begun to compose mazurkas, polonaises and waltzes. His first teacher, Wojciech Zywny, introduced him to the keyboard music of master composers such as J. S. Bach, Mozart, Beethoven, and Haydn. Mozart and Bach became idols for Chopin and he was particularly devoted to the study of Bach's music throughout his life. When Chopin was 12, he began to study composition with Joseph Elsner, who was the head of the Music Conservatory in Warsaw. Chopin entered the Conservatory in 1826 and graduated at the age of nineteen. By the time Chopin was twenty, he had already written fifty works for the piano.

In 1829, Chopin went to Vienna, where he gave two very successful piano concerts. It was also at this time that he arranged to have his variations on Mozart's *"La ci darem la mano"* published. This work attracted the attention of Robert Schumann, who reviewed the work in a magazine article and exclaimed "Hats off, gentlemen! A genius!"

The Polish rebellion against Russian domination, which ended in defeat, determined Chopin's decision to move to Paris in 1831, rather than return home to Poland. Paris became Chopin's home for the rest of his life. In Paris, his circle of acquaintances included composers Rossini, Cherubini, Bellini, Meyerbeer, Berlioz, and authors Victor Hugo and Heinrich Heine. He also established his close friendship with the piano virtuoso Franz Liszt. And, in 1836, began his famous romance with novelist Aurore Dupin - known more often by her published name, George Sand.

A brilliant pianist with unique poetic qualities, Chopin's delicate and frail body lacked the strength needed to play loud enough for large concert halls. Instead, Chopin established his reputation as a pianist by giving many performances in the salons of Parisian high society. As a result, Chopin moved though fashionable social circles and attracted many wealthy aristocratic piano students. Piano teaching was his chief source of income, although he was also well paid by publishers for his compositions.

Rarely familiar with good health throughout his life, Chopin was terminally ill with tuberculosis by 1847. Yet, he continued to play, teach and compose until close to the time of his death in 1849. Mozart's *Requiem* was performed at his funeral at the Madeleine. He was buried at Pere Lachaise between the graves of Cherubini and Bellini; however, at his own request, his heart was sent to Warsaw for entombment in his homeland.

The painting on the cover of this book is by Claude Monet (1840-1926) and is titled *Argenteuil* (1873). Monet was a famous French Impressionist and it was his painting *Impression, Le Havre* (1872) that gave the name to the French Impressionist movement.

Chopin was dedicated to writing music for the piano and rarely composed for any other instrument. He wrote over two-hundred works for the piano. Generally, he composed in specific genres. The following is a glossary of the types of pieces represented in this book.

MAZURKA. A Polish dance from Mazovia (near Warsaw). Always in triple meter with strong accents on usually weak beats (beat two or three). The dance is performed by four, eight or twelve couples and was originally accompanied by a type of bagpipe. The mazurka became a fashionable dance in European capitals during the 18th and 19th centuries and then evolved into an instrumental music genre. Chopin wrote over fifty mazurkas.

NOCTURNE. A romantic character piece for piano written in a melancholy or languid style with an expressive melody over a broken chord accompaniment. The name suggests night, and the music is usually quiet and meditative in character. The first nocturnes were written by John Field (1782 - 1837) from whom Chopin adopted the idea and the name. The title was also used by French composer Gabriel Fauré (1845 - 1924).

POLONAISE. A Polish national dance of stately and festive character. It originated in connection with court ceremonies and processions. Chopin made the polonaise a symbol of Polish heroism and chivalry. Typically, a polonaise is in moderate triple meter and consists of short phrases without upbeat. Chopin characterized his polonaises with the rhythmic pattern:

PRELUDE. A composition intended to precede a larger work or group of pieces. Preludes evolved from improvisations by musicians testing the tuning, touch or tone of their instrument. In the Baroque period, a prelude followed by a fugue or a suite of dances became the most common type. Typical of the Romantic period are sets of independent preludes written in all twenty-four keys, such as Chopin's Twenty-four Preludes, Op. 28. Other composers who wrote sets of preludes in all keys include Busoni, Heller, Hummel, and Rachmaninoff. Some twentieth-century composers, including Scriabin, Shostakovich, and Kabalevsky, wrote sets of preludes, but did not always follow the scheme of using all twenty-four keys. Claude Debussy wrote two books of *Twelve Preludes*, and differed from other composers by including descriptive titles for each prelude.

WALTZ. The most popular ballroom dance of the 19th century, the waltz originated ca. 1800 and has inspired many composers. Schubert was the first to write music specifically described as waltzes. Stylized waltzes are found in instrumental and orchestral music. Some of the most original for piano are those by Chopin.

WALTZ IN A MINOR
Opus Posthumous

Waltz in B Minor

Opus 69, No. 2

Waltz da Capo al Fine

MAZURKA IN F MAJOR
Opus 68, No. 3

Fine

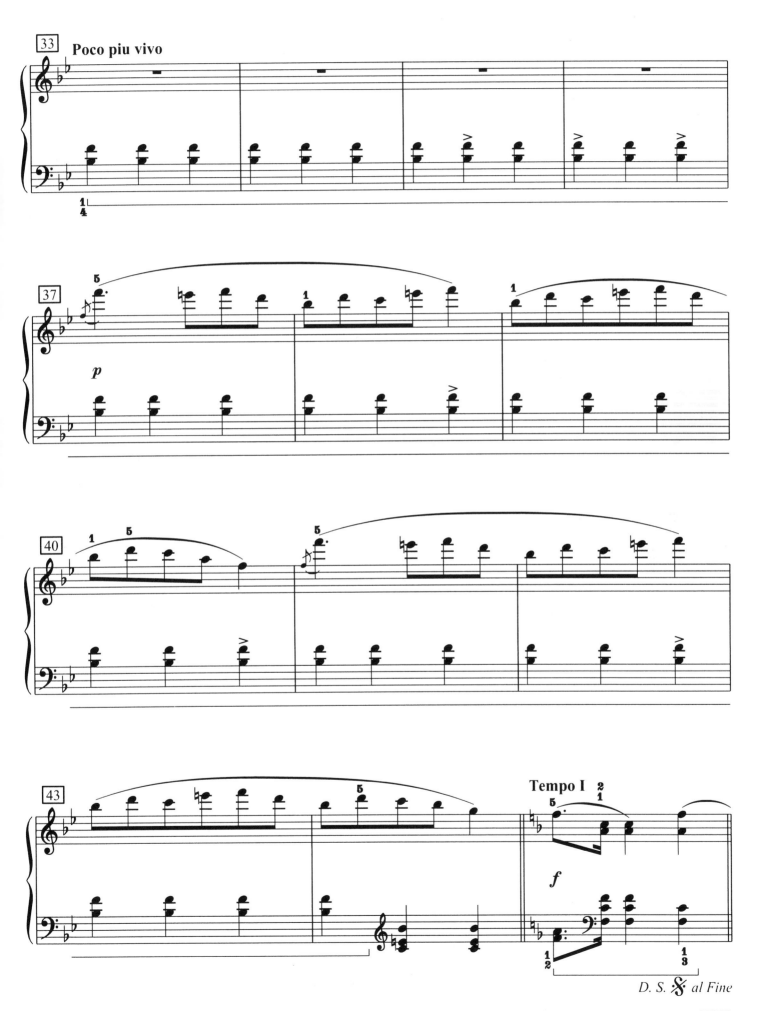

D. S. 𝄋 al Fine

MAZURKA IN A MINOR

Opus 67, No. 4

D. S. 𝄋 al Fine

Mazurka in G# Minor

Opus 33, No. 1

POLONAISE IN G MINOR

Opus Posthumous

Polonaise D. C. al fine

PRELUDE IN E MINOR

Opus 28, No. 4

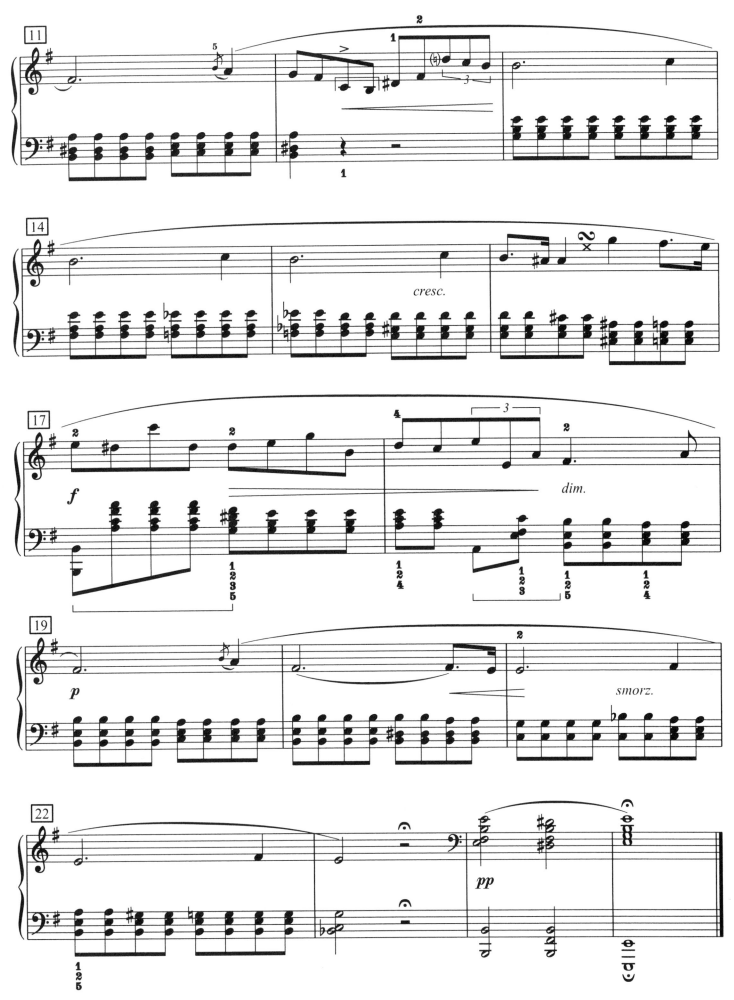

PRELUDE IN B MINOR

Opus 28, No. 6

PRELUDE IN A MAJOR
Opus 28, No. 7

PRELUDE IN C MINOR
Opus 28, No. 20

NOCTURNE IN C MINOR

Opus Posthumous

Andante sostenuto